CHESTER'S MANUSCRIPT

This Manuscript Book belongs to

Danny Gottschalk.

For explanations of musical terms and signs consult
Chester's Little Green Book (CH 55889)

© Copyright 1989 Chester Music Ltd   CH55981

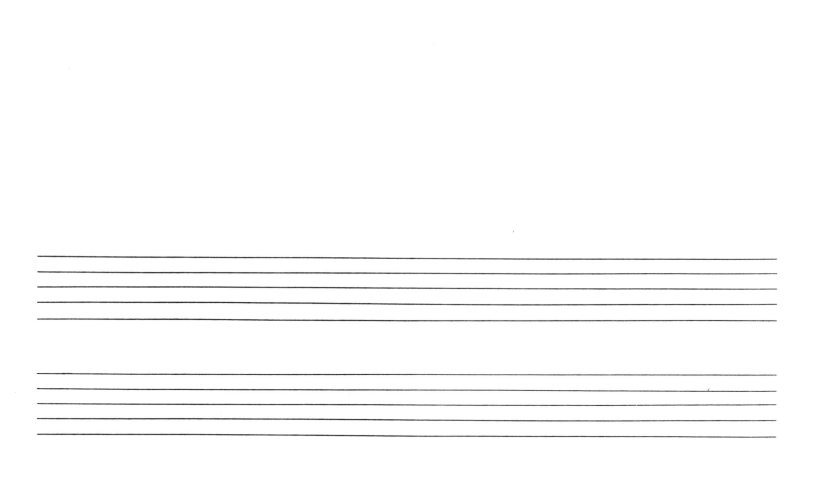

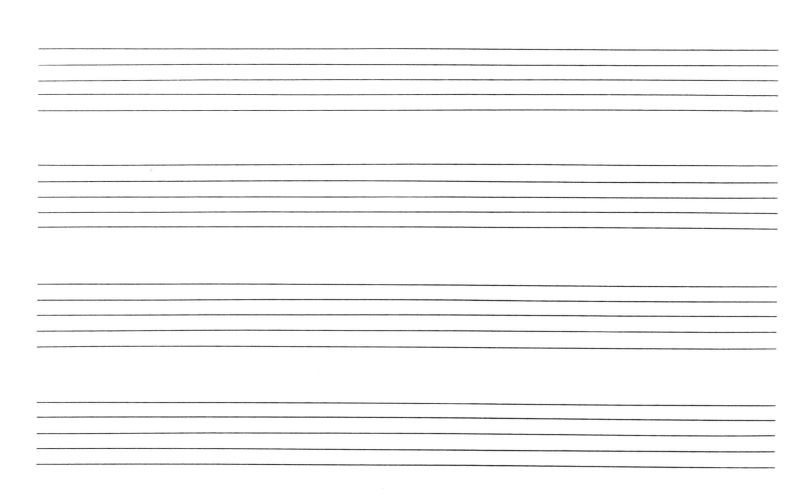

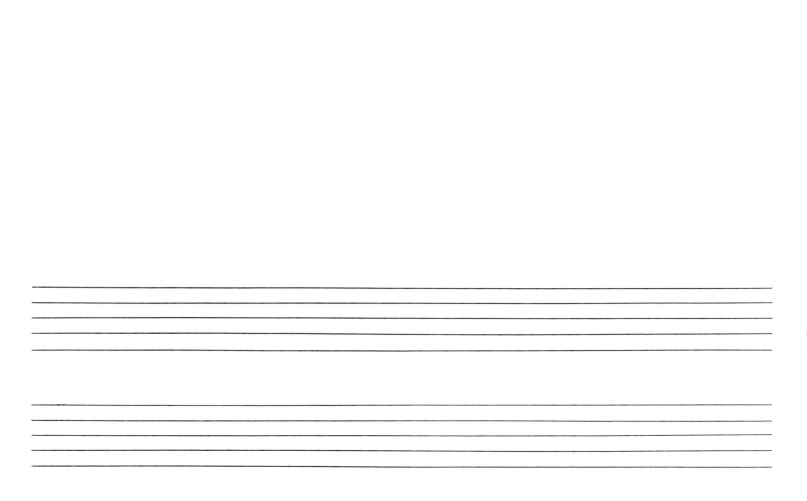

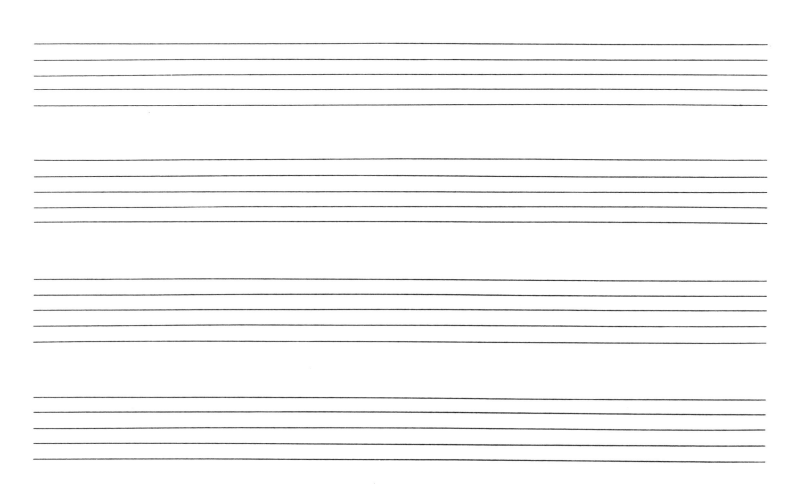

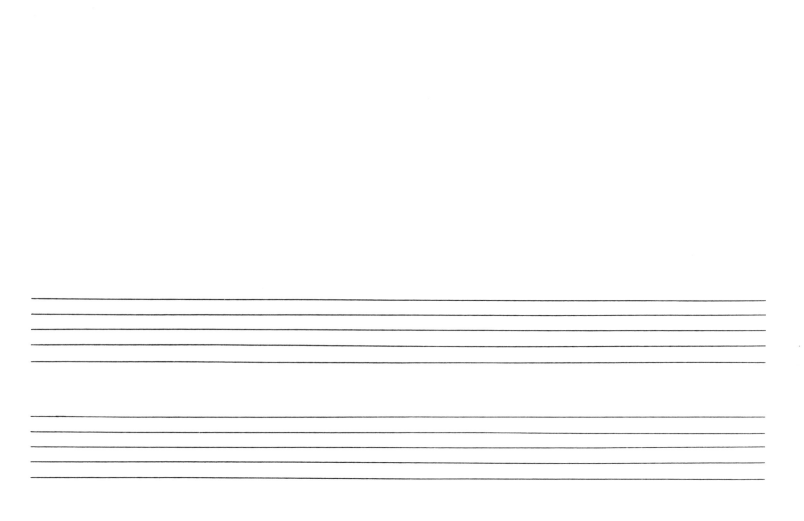

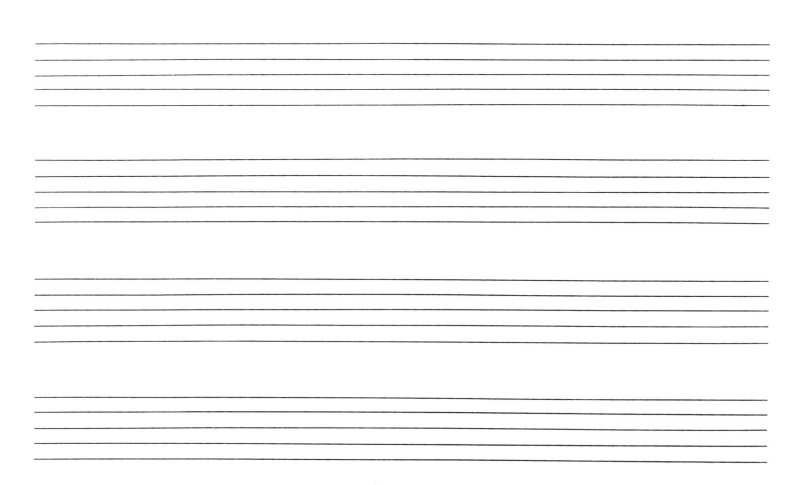

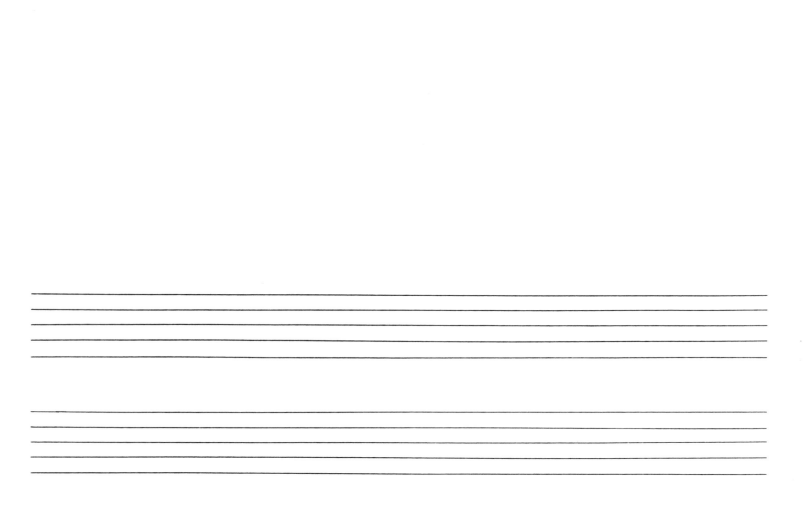

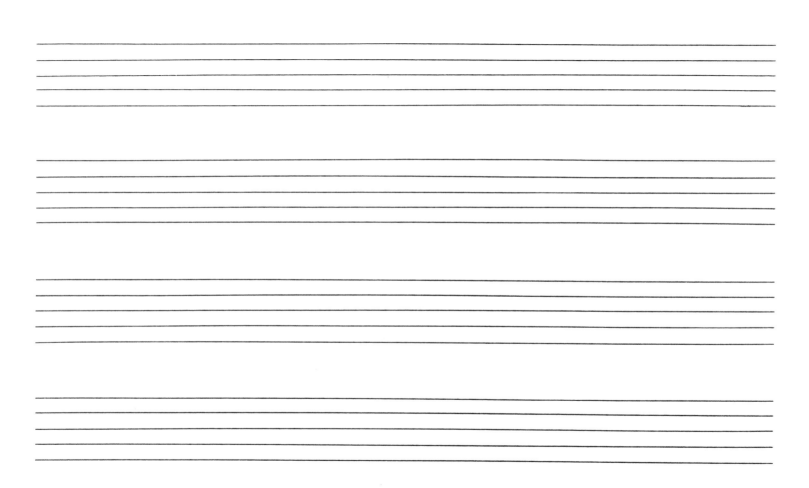

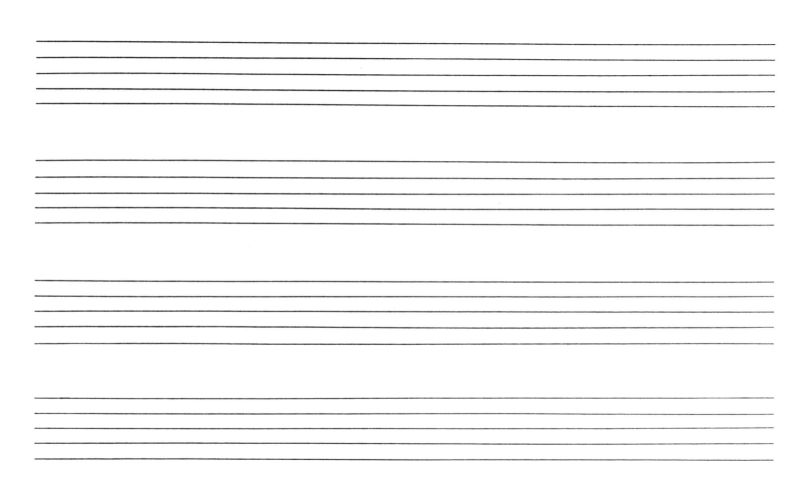

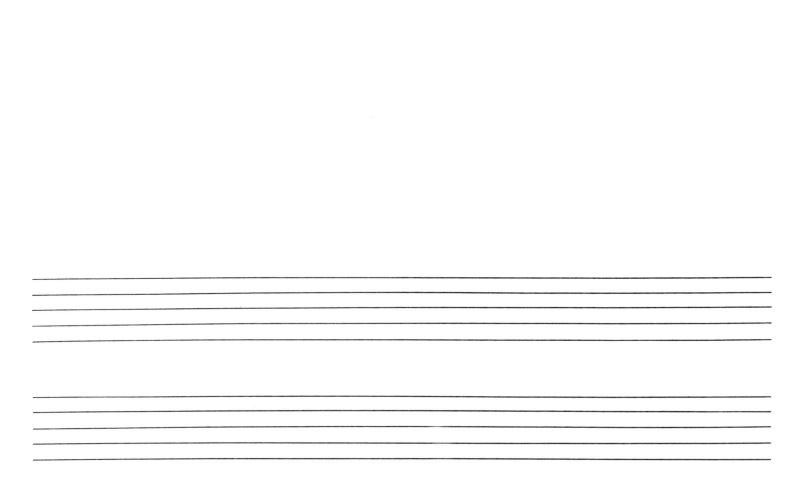

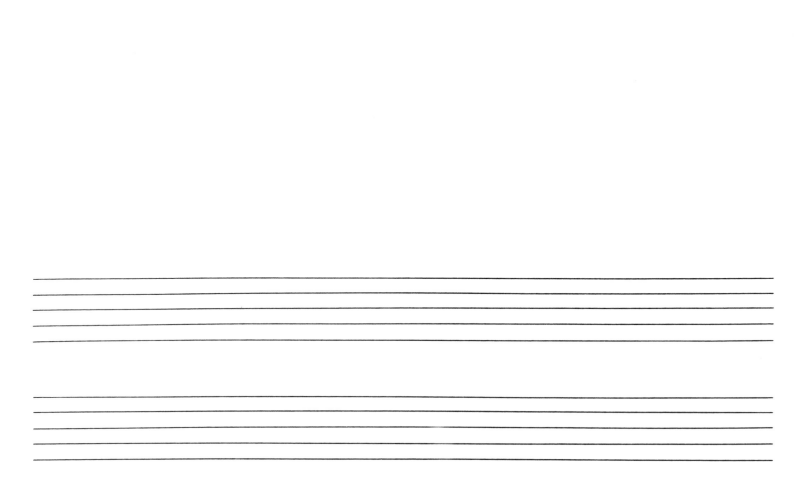

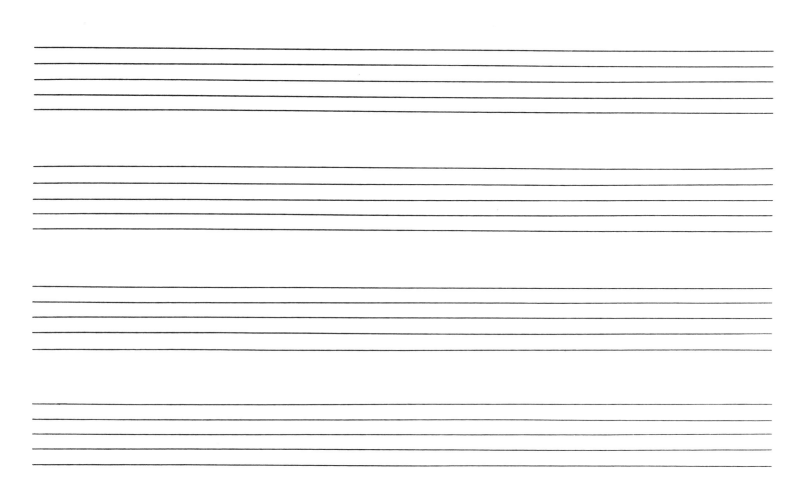

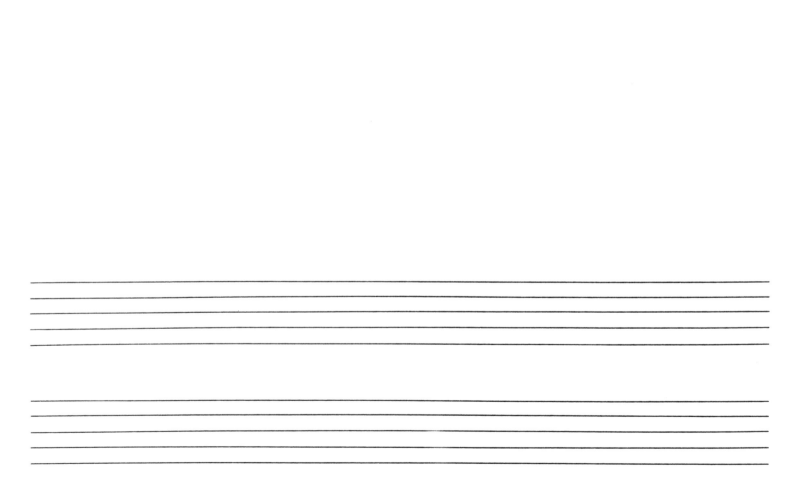

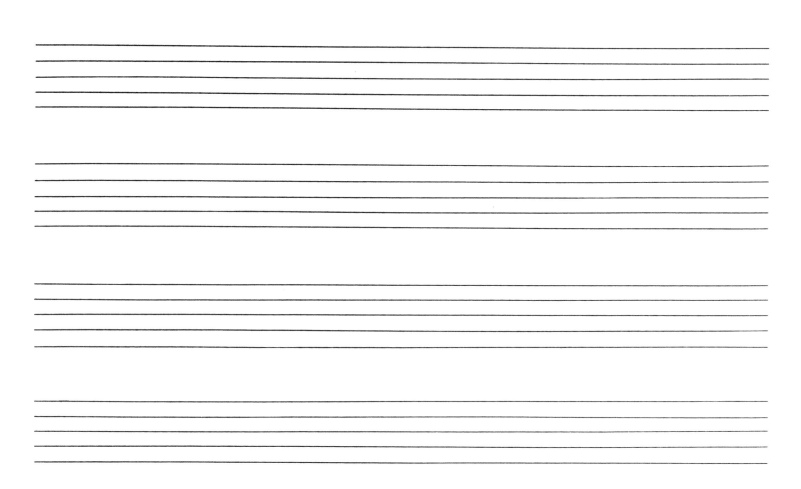

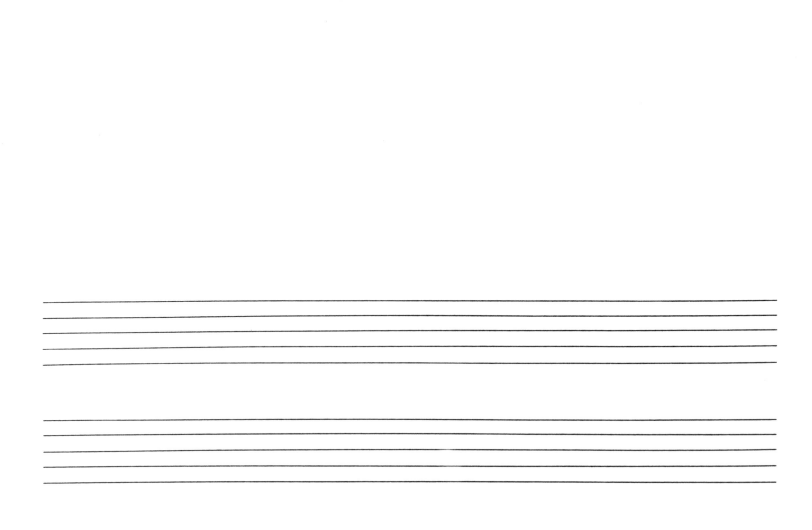

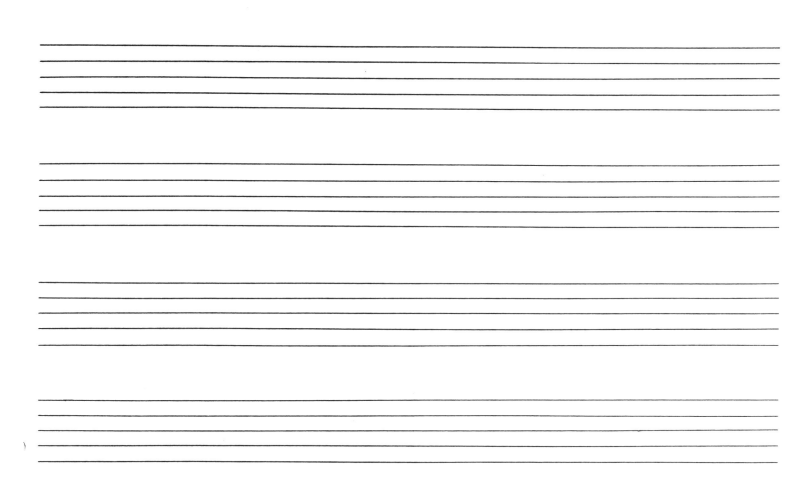

12/97(29418)